A VISIT FROM ST. NICHOLAS, *also known as "The Night Before Christmas," was written by Dr. Clement Clarke Moore in 1822 for his own children at Christmastime. The poem was first published anonymously in the* Sentinel, Troy, New York, *in 1823. It has become one of the first American children's classics and is now known throughout the world.*

Clement Moore, a graduate of Columbia College, was an outstanding scholar of Hebrew and Greek literature. But of all his many works, the verse, A VISIT FROM ST. NICHOLAS, *brought him his greatest fame.*

Paul Galdone, the illustrator of this book, lives in Rockland County, New York. For a number of years he resided in New York City, near the place where Dr. Moore wrote this poem. He enjoys illustrating American classics and he has illustrated the works of Nathaniel Hawthorne, Oliver Wendell Holmes, Henry Wadsworth Longfellow, and Edgar Allan Poe.

For Eileen, Peggy, Ann, Eleanor, Mary Jane, Marie, Leigh, Marion, Delores, and Susan

Library of Congress Catalog Card Number: 68-24348

A Visit from St. NICHOLAS

by Clement C. Moore

Paul Galdone drew the pictures

McGRAW-HILL BOOK COMPANY

New York • Toronto • London • Sydney

T was the night before Christmas,
when all through the house

Not a creature was stirring,

not even

a mouse.

The stockings were hung by the chimney with care,
In hopes that St. Nicholas soon would be there.

The children were nestled all snug in their beds,
While visions of sugarplums danced in their heads.

And Mamma in her kerchief, and I in my cap,
Had just settled our brains for a long winter's nap.

When out on the lawn there arose such a clatter,
I sprang from my bed to see what was the matter.

Away to the window I flew like a flash,
Tore open the shutters, and threw up the sash.

The moon on the breast of the new-fallen snow
Gave a luster of midday to objects below,

When what to my wondering eyes did appear,
But a miniature sleigh and eight tiny reindeer,

With a little old driver, so lively and quick,
I knew in a moment it must be St. Nick.

More rapid than eagles his coursers they came,
And he whistled, and shouted, and called them by name:

"Now, Dasher! now, Dancer! now, Prancer and Vixen!
On, Comet! on, Cupid! on, Donder and Blitzen!

To the top of the porch! to the top of the wall!
Now dash away! dash away! dash away, all!"

As dry leaves that before the wild hurricane fly,
When they meet with an obstacle, mount to the sky,

So up to the housetop the coursers they flew,
With the sleigh full of toys, and St. Nicholas too.

And then, in a twinkling, I heard on the roof
The prancing and pawing of each little hoof.

As I drew in my head and was turning around,
Down the chimney St. Nicholas came with a bound.

He was dressed all in fur, from his head to his foot,
And his clothes were all tarnished with ashes and soot;

A bundle of toys he had flung on his back,
And he looked like a peddler just opening his pack.

His eyes—how they twinkled! his dimples—how merry!
His cheeks were like roses, his nose like a cherry!

His droll little mouth was drawn up like a bow,
And the beard on his chin was as white as the snow.

The stump of a pipe he held tight in his teeth,
And the smoke, it encircled his head like a wreath;

He had a broad face and a little round belly
That shook, when he laughed, like a bowl full of jelly.

He was chubby and plump, a right jolly old elf,
And I laughed when I saw him, in spite of myself;

A wink of his eye and a twist of his head
Soon gave me to know I had nothing to dread.

He spoke not a word, but went straight to his work,
And filled all the stockings; then turned with a jerk.

And laying a finger aside of his nose,
And giving a nod, up the chimney he rose.

He sprang to his sleigh, to his team gave a whistle,
And away they all flew like the down of a thistle.

But I heard him exclaim ere he drove out of sight,

"HAPPY CHRISTMAS TO ALL,
AND TO ALL A GOOD-NIGHT!"

100

8   12/99
9   9/07 (8/10)